Counting to 20

CW00350530

▶ Count the pictures. Write the num

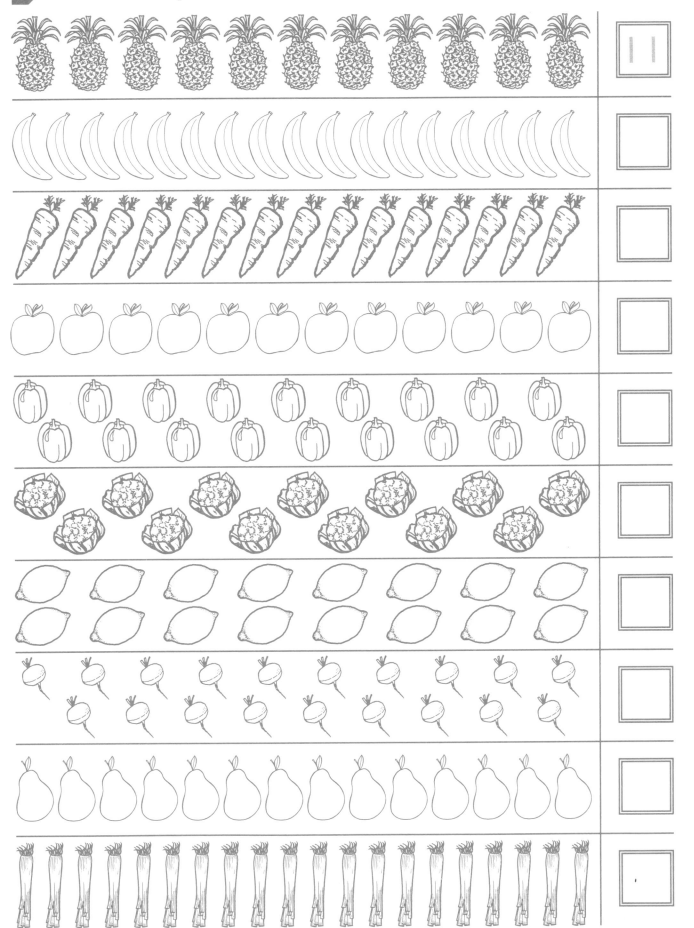

3

▶ **Continue the numbers.**

| 7 | 8 | 9 | 10 | 11 | 12 | | | | |

Houses: 11, 12, 13, 14

Balloons: 10, 11

Caterpillar: 9, 10, 11, 12

Snake: 12, 13

▶ **Fill in the missing numbers.**

| 6 | 7 | 8 | | | | 12 | | | |

10   11   13   15   18   20

▶ **Write the number after:**

| 10 | 11 | | 15 | | | 18 | | | 11 | | | 16 | |
| 12 | | | 19 | | | 14 | | | 17 | | | 13 | |

▶ **Write the number before:**

| 18 | 17 | | 15 | | | | 11 | | | 13 | | | 17 |
| 19 | | | 12 | | | | 16 | | | 20 | | | 14 |

▶ On the caterpillar, colour the numbers before 17 and after 12.
On the snake, colour the numbers before 13 and after 19.

4

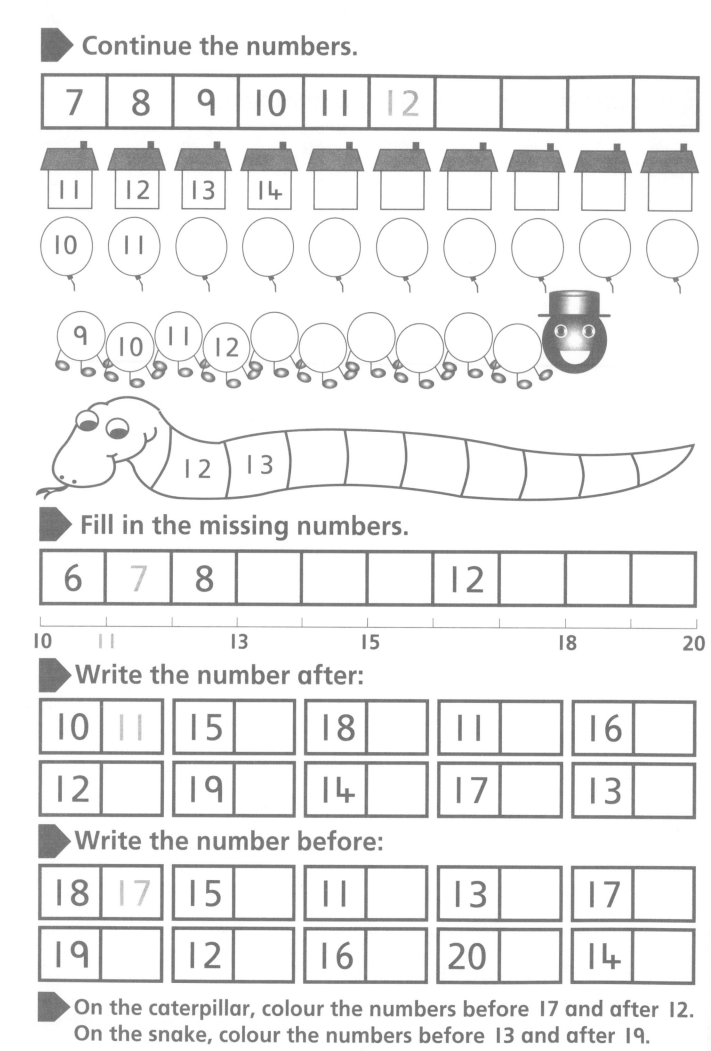

How many spots?

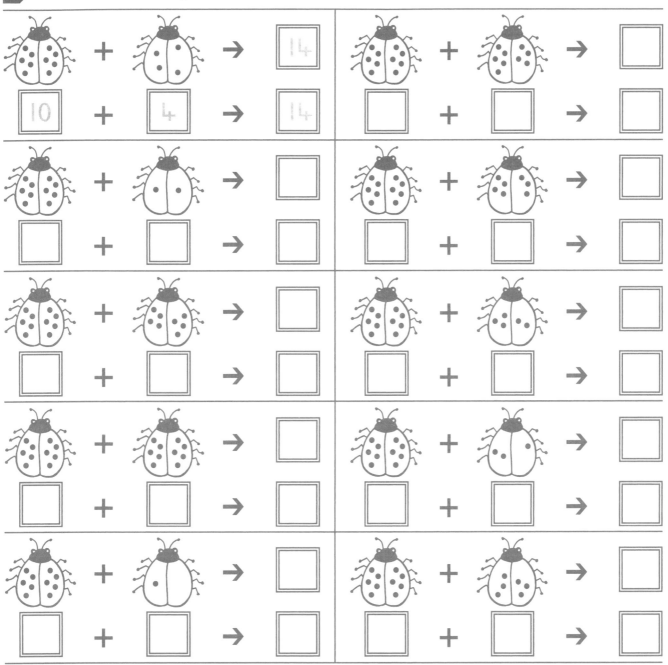

Complete the sums.

10 + 6 → 16   10 + 10 → ☐   10 + 4 → ☐   7 + 10 → ☐

5 + 10 → ☐   3 + 10 → ☐   10 + 2 → ☐   10 + 1 → ☐

Find the missing number.

10 + 3 → 13   10 + ☐ → 18   10 + ☐ → 20

5

Tens and ones

▶ **Write how many tens and ones.**

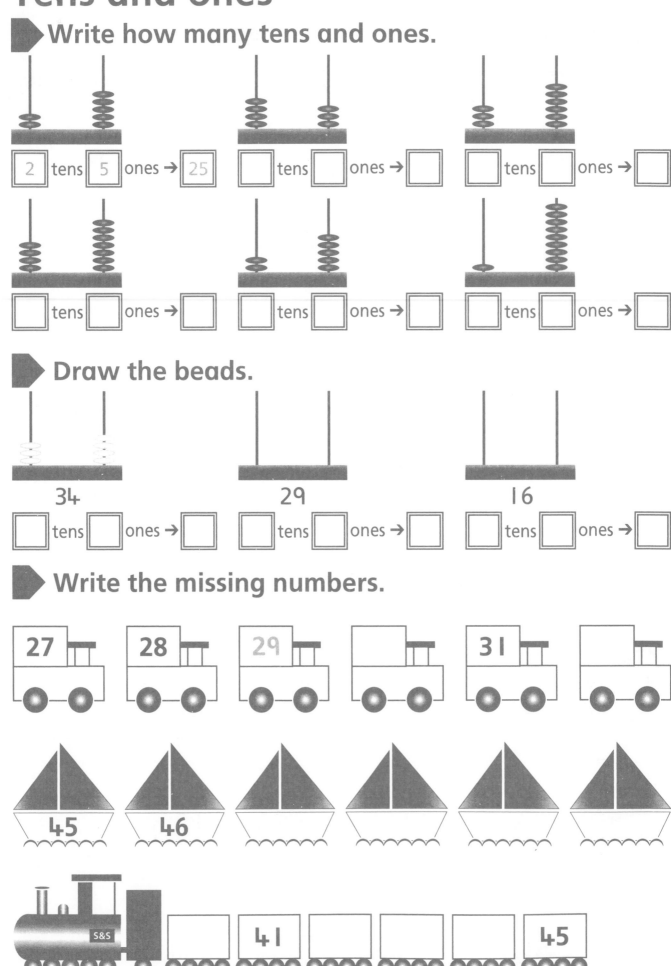

| 2 | tens | 5 | ones → | 25 |

| | tens | | ones → | |

| | tens | | ones → | |

| | tens | | ones → | |

| | tens | | ones → | |

| | tens | | ones → | |

▶ **Draw the beads.**

34

29

16

| | tens | | ones → | |

| | tens | | ones → | |

| | tens | | ones → | |

▶ **Write the missing numbers.**

27   28   29   ☐   31   ☐

45   46   ☐   ☐   ☐   ☐

S&S   ☐   41   ☐   ☐   ☐   45

6

Money

▶ Draw the coins to show 5p in each purse.

  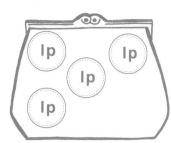 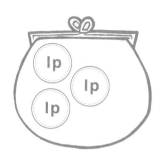

▶ How much money is there in each money box?

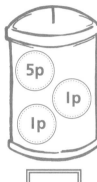   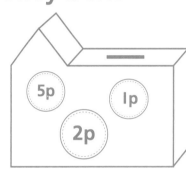

7 p p p p

▶ Draw the coins to pay for these.
Use 1p 2p 5p

 7p  |  9p

 5p |  10p

 8p |  6p

Tens and ones

▶ Use rods to work out the answers.

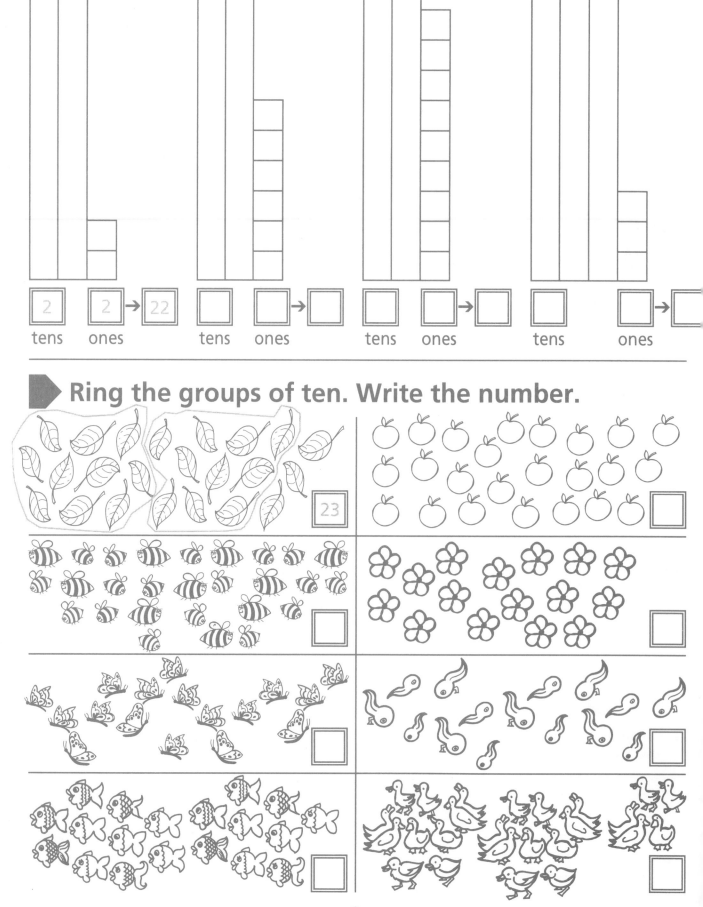

2	2 → 22			→			→			→
tens	ones		tens	ones		tens	ones		tens	ones	

▶ Ring the groups of ten. Write the number.

23

8

Adding and taking 10

 Write the answer.

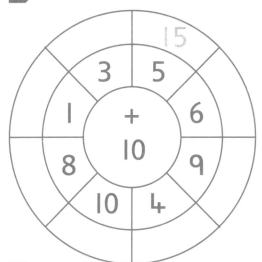

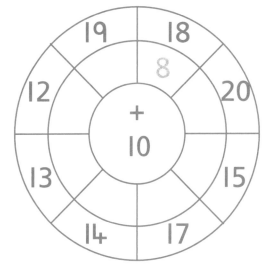 Find the missing number.

▶ Count on.

0 1 2 3 4 5 6 7 8 9 10 11 12 13 14 15 16 17 18 19 20 21 22 23 24 25 26 27 28 29 30

Count on 10	Count on 10	Count on 10
5 → 15	6 →	13 →
8 →	17 →	2 →
4 →	0 →	12 →
15 →	11 →	14 →

▶ Count back.

0 1 2 3 4 5 6 7 8 9 10 11 12 13 14 15 16 17 18 19 20 21 22 23 24 25 26 27 28 29 30

Count back 10	Count back 10	Count back 10
15 → 5	19 →	16 →
17 →	21 →	22 →
11 →	14 →	18 →
10 →	27 →	25 →

▶ Add and take away.

17 − 10 → ☐ 7 ☐   21 − 10 → ☐   16 + 10 → ☐   14 − 10 → ☐

15 + 10 → ☐   9 + 10 → ☐   27 − 10 → ☐   12 + 10 → ☐

9

Solve the problem

16	people
5	people wearing hats
11	people without hats

5 + 11 → 16

14	sandcastles
	sandcastles with flags
	sandcastles without flags

7 + ☐ → 14

	candles
	candles lit
	candles not lit

6 + ☐ → 12

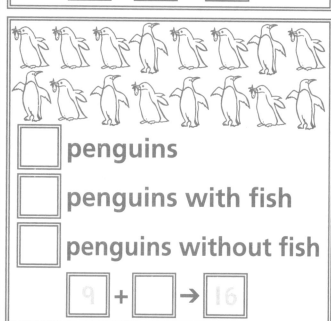

	penguins
	penguins with fish
	penguins without fish

9 + ☐ → 16

 Magic Squares.

Write down numbers in each space to make all the lines add up to 6.

1	3	2
	2	
2		

Write down numbers in each space to make all the lines add up to 10.

4			
2			
1			

10

Measuring

Shorter and longer than a metre.

▶ **Use a metre stick to find 4 things:**

shorter than a metre.
Draw them.

longer than a metre.
Draw them.

▶ **How many make a metre?**
Colour a space for each one.

		1	2	3	4	5	6	7	8	9	10	11	12	13	14	15	16	17	18	19	20
	pencil																				
	crayon																				
	paintbrush																				
	ruler																				
	book																				
	straw																				

▶ **Use a metre stick to measure. Find out which are shorter**
or longer than a metre. Colour the correct space.

	shorter than a metre	longer than a metre	about 1 metre
table			
bookcase			
shoe			
door			
mat			

11

Area

▶ Colour the largest surface area red.
Colour the smallest surface area blue.

▶ How many envelopes ✉ will cover the surface area?

	estimate	measure
table		
book		
chair seat		
mat		
your own choice		
your own choice		
your own choice		

▶ Which has the largest surface area?

▶ Which has the smallest surface area?

12

Days of the week

▶ **Write the missing days of the week.**

Sunday

Monday

[   ]

Friday   Wednesday

[   ]

[   ]   [   ]

Wednesday   Saturday

[   ]   [   ]

Monday

▶ **Write the day after:**

Monday _____   Saturday_____

Wednesday _____   Friday _____

▶ **Write the day before:**

Sunday _____   Thursday_____

Monday _____   Tuesday _____

▶ **Which days do you go to school?**

_____ _____   _____

_____ _____

▶ **Which days are the weekend?**

_____ _____

▶ **On which day is your birthday this year?**

_____

▶ **On which day were you born?**

_____

13

Time

 Write the time.

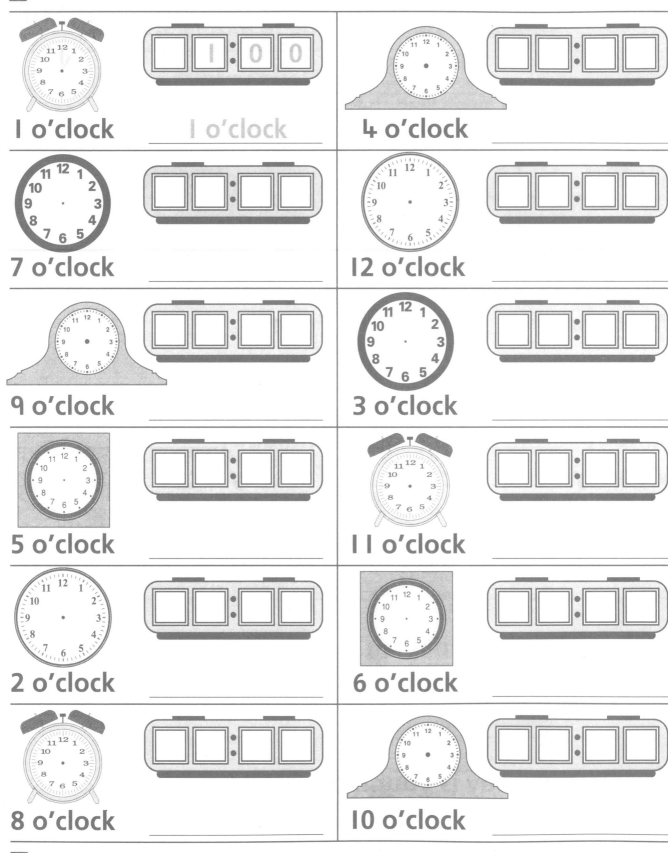

1 o'clock — 1 o'clock	4 o'clock
7 o'clock	12 o'clock
9 o'clock	3 o'clock
5 o'clock	11 o'clock
2 o'clock	6 o'clock
8 o'clock	10 o'clock

 Draw a red ring round the clock showing the time nearest to when school starts.

All take aways

▶ **Match to find the answer.**

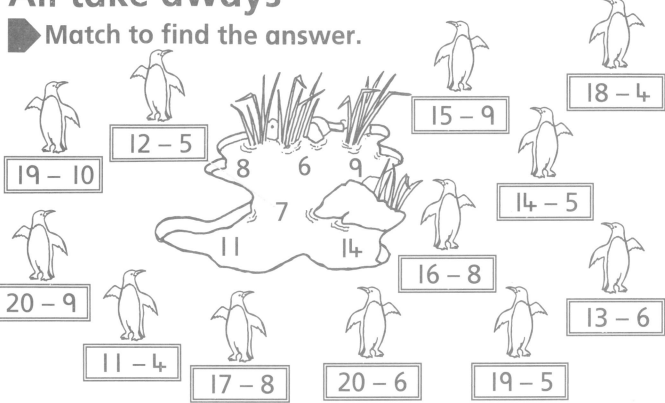

19 – 10   12 – 5   15 – 9   18 – 4   14 – 5

20 – 9   11 – 4   17 – 8   20 – 6   19 – 5   16 – 8   13 – 6

Pond numbers: 8 6 9 7 11 14

16 – 9 →☐   20 – 7 →☐   12 – 9 →☐

14 – 7 →☐   13 – 11 →☐   15 – 8 →☐

18 – 2 →☐   19 – 15 →☐   18 – 13 →☐

15 – 4 →☐   11 – 7 →☐   14 – 5 →☐

16 – 0 →☐   18 – 11 →☐   20 – 11 →☐

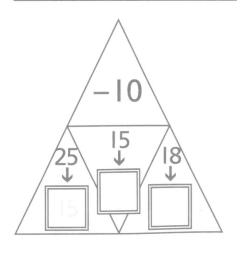

– 10 : 25→15 15→☐ 18→☐

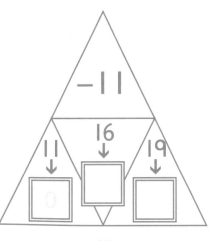

– 11 : 11→0 16→☐ 19→☐

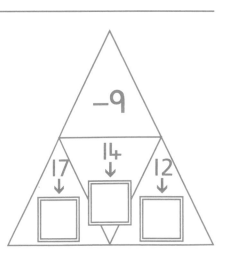

– 9 : 17→☐ 14→☐ 12→☐

15

Add and take away

15 – 5 → ☐	13 – 7 → ☐	18 – 9 → ☐
19 + 1 → ☐	14 + 6 → ☐	12 + 6 → ☐
17 – 4 → ☐	9 + 7 → ☐	5 + 7 → ☐
13 – 12 → ☐	15 – 8 → ☐	19 – 7 → ☐
14 – 5 → ☐	10 + 9 → ☐	16 – 8 → ☐

▶ **Use these numbers to make some number sentences.**

19 1 20   20 – 1 → 19   4 13 17 _____

15 10 5 _____   12 2 10 _____

8 2 10 _____   3 9 12 _____

20 3 17 _____   6 14 8 _____

▶ **Match the numbers to their nearest ten.**

19   (10)   13

14

11   32   (20)   6   28

26   17

14   25   (30)   29   34   16

16

Count on and back

Count on.

10 + 6 → 16	9 + 7 → ☐	14 + 3 → ☐
12 + 4 → ☐	3 + 12 → ☐	11 + 9 → ☐
17 + 2 → ☐	8 + 4 → ☐	15 + 4 → ☐
11 + 5 → ☐	16 + 3 → ☐	13 + 4 → ☐
13 + 7 → ☐	10 + 10 → ☐	18 + 2 → ☐

Count back.

18 − 6 → 12	12 − 8 → ☐	14 − 6 → ☐
19 − 3 → ☐	15 − 7 → ☐	12 − 5 → ☐
15 − 2 → ☐	16 − 6 → ☐	19 − 8 → ☐
11 − 7 → ☐	11 − 5 → ☐	20 − 11 → ☐
19 − 11 → ☐	13 − 7 → ☐	15 − 5 → ☐

Count on and back.

7 + 8 → 15	14 − ☐ → 6	13 + ☐ → 19
6 + ☐ → 13	13 − ☐ → 3	20 − ☐ → 15
18 − ☐ → 6	5 + ☐ → 19	13 + ☐ → 18
12 + ☐ → 17	17 − ☐ → 11	20 − ☐ → 12
19 − ☐ → 10	2 + ☐ → 20	9 + ☐ → 17

17

Solve the problem

▶ Write your own number story for these pictures.

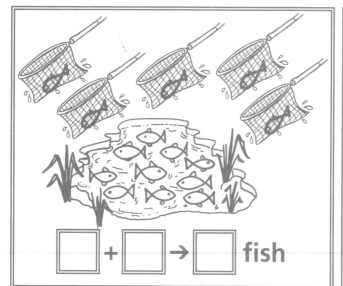

☐ + ☐ → ☐ fish

☐ + ☐ → ☐ ladybirds

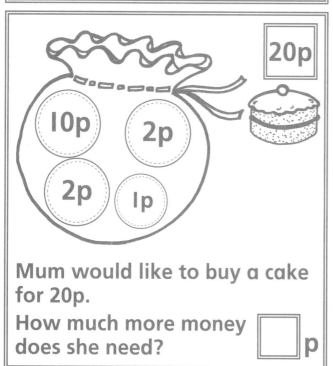

Mum would like to buy a cake for 20p.

How much more money does she need? ☐ p

Jack spends 15p on his ice cream.

How much change does he have left? ☐ p

▶ Finish these number strips.

| 5 | 7 | 9 | 11 | __ | __ | __ | __ |

| 1 + 3 → ☐ | + 2 → 6 + 3 → 9 + ☐ → 18 |

| 2 | 4 | 6 | 8 | __ | __ | __ | __ |

Money

Match to show which purses hold 10p.

How much money in each purse?

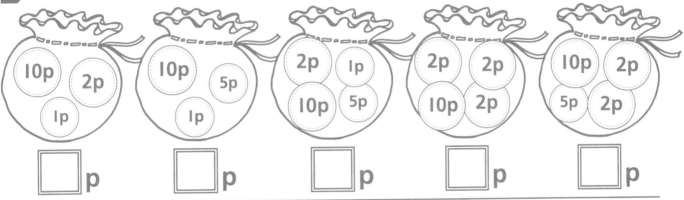

Draw the coins to pay for these. Use 10p, 5p, 2p and 1p coins.

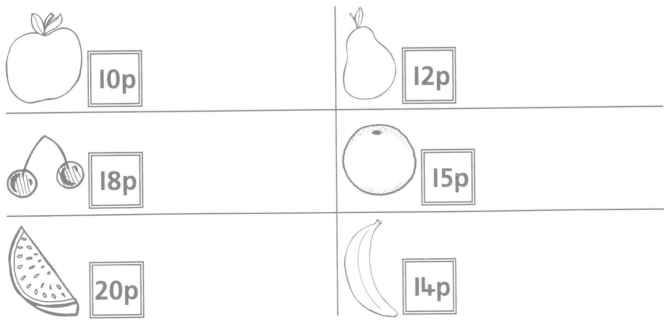

Draw the coins in the money boxes.
Use 10p, 5p, 2p and 1p coins.

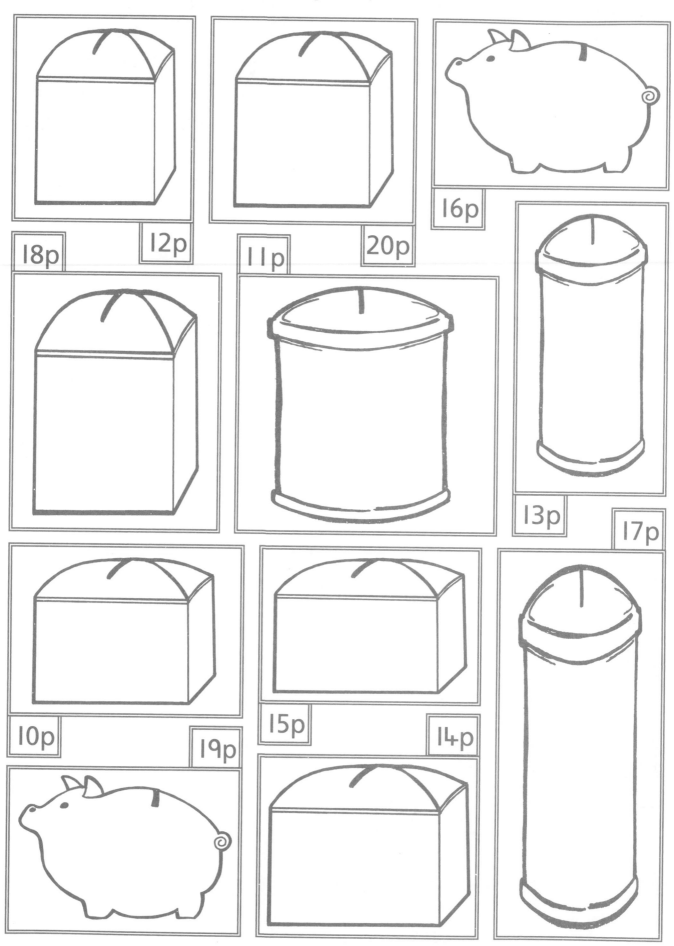

18p

12p

11p

20p

16p

13p

17p

10p

19p

15p

14p

▶ What have you spent?

fish 7p	rabbit 4p	cat 8p	mouse 5p
tortoise 9p	snake 10p	bird 6p	dog 10p

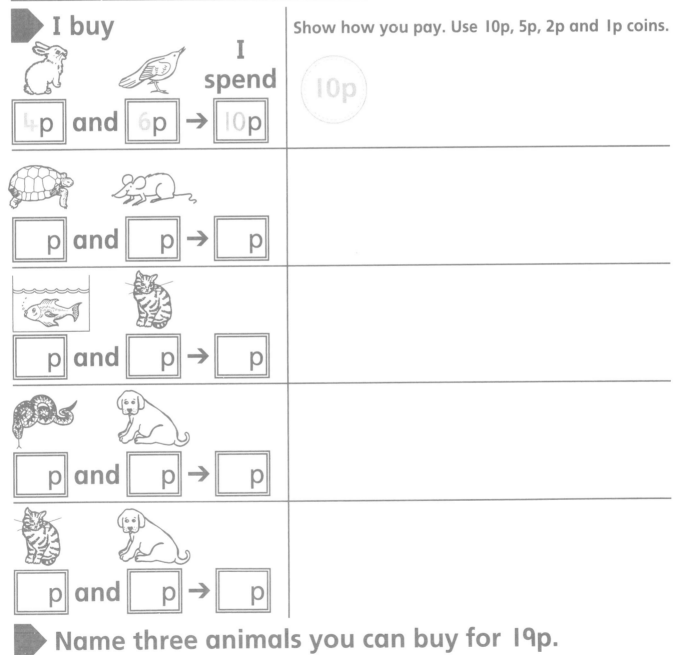

▶ I buy

Show how you pay. Use 10p, 5p, 2p and 1p coins.

I spend

4p and 6p → 10p   ⬭ 10p

___ p and ___ p → ___ p

___ p and ___ p → ___ p

___ p and ___ p → ___ p

___ p and ___ p → ___ p

▶ Name three animals you can buy for 19p.

_____   _____   _____

Colour the coins to pay.

11p	1p	2p	10p	10p	2p	5p
16p	5p	2p	2p	1p	10p	5p
13p	1p	1p	5p	10p	2p	10p
19p	2p	1p	1p	2p	5p	10p
17p	10p	2p	1p	1p	1p	5p

Draw how much change you need.

Change from 20p	Change from 20p
19p — 1p	16p
Change from 15p	Change from 20p
11p	17p

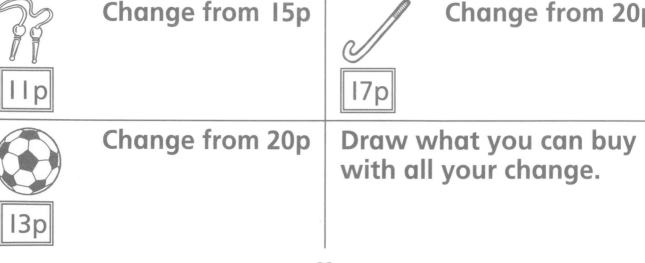

Change from 20p	Draw what you can buy with all your change.
13p	

22

Weighing

▶ Use a kilogram weight to find things weighing more than, less than and the same as one kilogram.
Colour a space to show the correct answer.

	less than a kilogram	more than a kilogram	about a kilogram		less than a kilogram	more than a kilogram	about a kilogram
bag of flour				packet of rice			
packet of tea				packet of spaghetti			
box of icing sugar				drum of salt			

▶ How many balance a kilogram?
Estimate first, then balance.

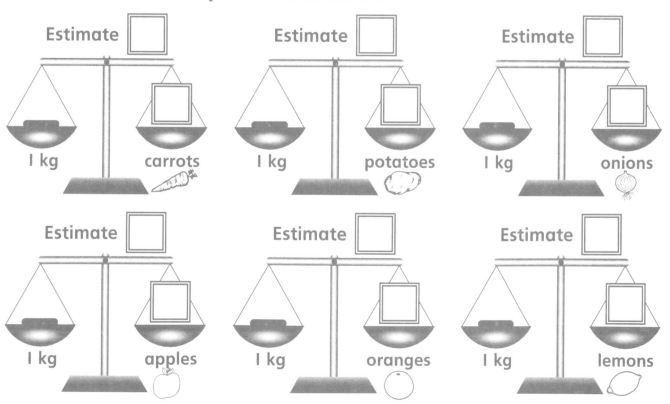

Estimate ☐   1 kg   carrots

Estimate ☐   1 kg   potatoes

Estimate ☐   1 kg   onions

Estimate ☐   1 kg   apples

Estimate ☐   1 kg   oranges

Estimate ☐   1 kg   lemons

23

Capacity

▶ Use a tablespoon and then an eggcup to fill each container.
Write down how many it takes.

To fill	🥄 tablespoons	🥚 eggcups
small jug		
cup		
mug		
yoghurt carton		

The
_____
_____
held most.
The
_____
_____
held least.

▶ Use a mug to measure.
Estimate first and then measure.

To fill	estimate 🍵	measure 🍵
jug		
small bottle		
work tray		
ice-cream container		
squash container		
pudding basin		
large bottle		
bucket		

I estimated
_____
correctly.

The
_____
_____
held most.

The
_____
_____
held least.

3D Shapes

▶ **Match the shapes to their names.**

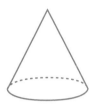
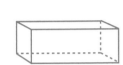

cylinder
cuboid
sphere
cone
cube

▶ **How many faces does each shape have?**
Write the number.

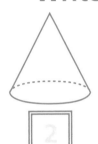

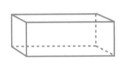

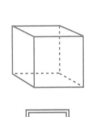

| 2 | | | | |

▶ **Colour the shapes.**

sphere → blue   cuboid → red   cylinder → orange
cube → yellow   cone → green

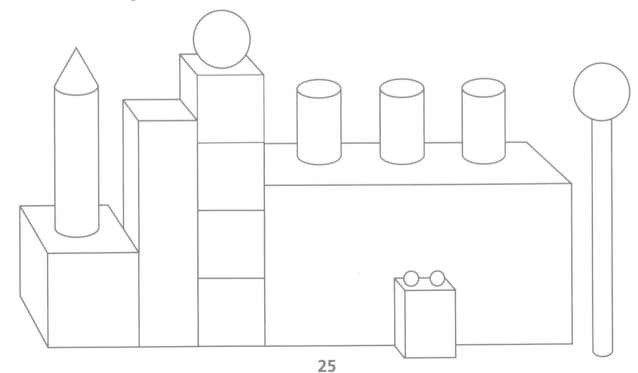

2D Shapes

▶ **Count the sides. Write the name.**

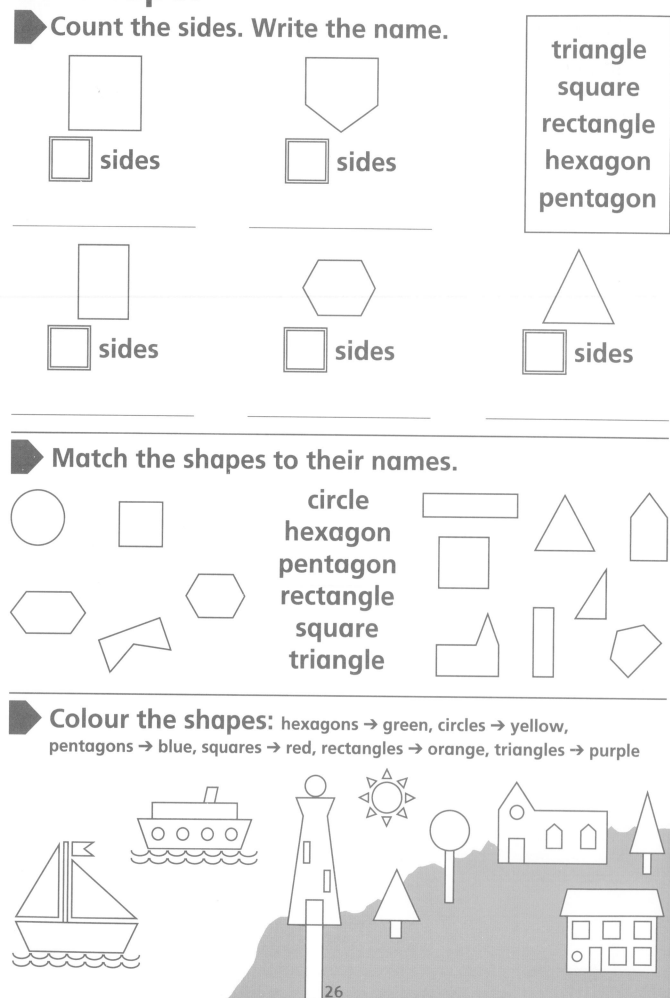

☐ sides

☐ sides

triangle
square
rectangle
hexagon
pentagon

☐ sides

☐ sides

☐ sides

▶ **Match the shapes to their names.**

circle
hexagon
pentagon
rectangle
square
triangle

▶ **Colour the shapes:** hexagons → green, circles → yellow, pentagons → blue, squares → red, rectangles → orange, triangles → purple

26

Shapes and patterns

▶ Make a triangle.
Make a pentagon.

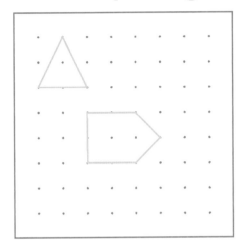

▶ Make a square.
Make a hexagon.

▶ Trace over the shapes.
Draw the other half.

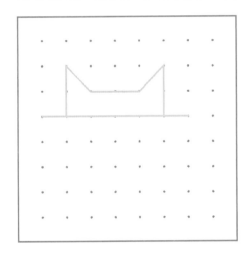

▶ Make up your own
reflections here.

Money

▶ **Make all the boxes add up to 20p.**

Use 1p, 2p, 5p and 10p coins.

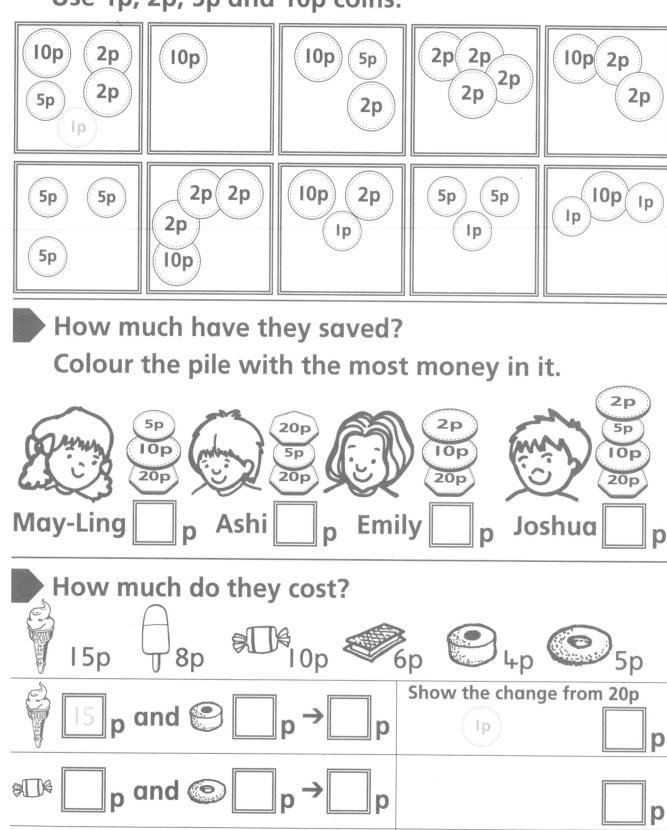

▶ **How much have they saved?**

Colour the pile with the most money in it.

May-Ling ☐ p   Ashi ☐ p   Emily ☐ p   Joshua ☐ p

▶ **How much do they cost?**

🍦 15p   🍡 8p   🍬 10p   🧇 6p   🍥 4p   🍩 5p

	Show the change from 20p
🍦 15 p and 🍥 ☐ p → ☐ p	1p ☐ p
🍬 ☐ p and 🍩 ☐ p → ☐ p	☐ p
🍡 ☐ p and 🧇 ☐ p → ☐ p	☐ p

Grand Sale

▶ Take 10p off everything.

 **25p** socks *15p*

 **46p** shoes

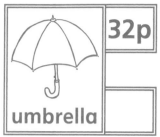 **32p** umbrella

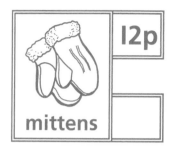 **12p** mittens

▶ Take 5p off everything.

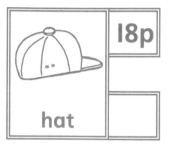 **18p** hat

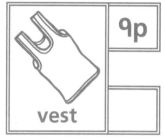 **9p** vest

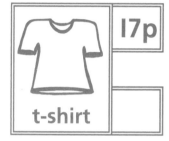 **17p** t-shirt

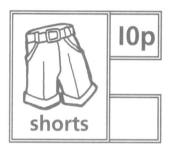 **10p** shorts

▶ What did you buy in the sale?

Spend 17p	Spend 26p	Spend 49p
and	and	and

▶ How much change from 20p?

 and

15 p + *2* p → *17* p   20p − *17* p → *3* p

 and

☐ p + ☐ p → ☐ p   20p − ☐ p → ☐ p

 and

☐ p + ☐ p → ☐ p   20p − ☐ p → ☐ p

29

Number Machines

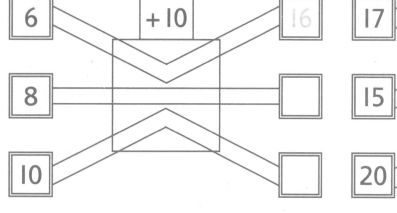

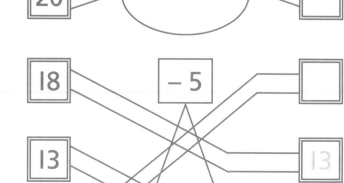

| 4 | 5 | 7 | 8 | 10 | 12 |

▶ **Use any 2 numbers to make the sum.**

$\boxed{4} + \boxed{8} \rightarrow 12$ $\boxed{} + \boxed{} \rightarrow 17$ $\boxed{} + \boxed{} \rightarrow 11$

$\boxed{} + \boxed{} \rightarrow 18$ $\boxed{} + \boxed{} \rightarrow 15$ $\boxed{} + \boxed{} \rightarrow 20$

▶ **Match the sum to the answer.**

| 15 + 4 | | 14 + 3 |

   △ 4

   △ 5

| 20 − 11 | | 11 − 6 |

   △ 9

   △ 18

| 13 − 9 | | 9 + 9 |

   △ 17

   △ 19